Jack The More

Exercise

by **Sarah, Duchess of York**

Illustrated by Ian Cunliffe

Jack Takes More Exercise

helping hand books

First published in Great Britain 2007 by Lloyds Pharmacy Ltd
Sapphire Court, Walsgrave Triangle, Coventry CV2 2TX

www.lloydspharmacy.com

In consultation with Cameron Wilson Ltd

Illustrated by Ian Cunliffe

'Ten Helpful Hints' contributed by Dr. Richard Woolfson,
child psychologist, Fellow of the British Psychological Society.

Printed in China

British Library Cataloguing in Publication Data
A catalogue record for this book is available from the British Library

ISBN 978-1-906260-08-8

All children face many new experiences as they grow up and helping them to understand and deal with each is one of the most demanding and rewarding things we do as parents. The helping hand books are for both children and parents to read, perhaps together. Each simple story describes a childhood experience and shows some of the ways in which to make it a positive one. I do hope these books encourage children and parents to talk about these sometimes difficult issues; talking together goes a long way to finding a solution.

Sarah

Sarah, Duchess of York

Jack loved television.
And computers.
And books.
His idea of the
perfect day was
to sit at home
and do all three!

When he was at school, like everyone else, he had to go outside at break time but even then he would try and take a book with him.

Jack didn't have very many friends because the things he liked to do didn't need friends.

Jack's Mum and Dad worried about this but, as they told each other, Jack seemed happy. They had told him often enough about exercise being important, but he took little notice.

Jack's Dad was away a lot but when he came home he liked to settle down in front of the television.

The only thing that
really upset Jack was
the weekly P.E. class at school.

Every week, he used to try hard to persuade
his Mum that he should be excused. He felt that
he was not as good as others at anything and it
made him not even want to try.

Sometimes he seemed so upset that his Mum
would write a note to excuse him.

One day, during the school holidays, there was a lot of banging and crashing from the house next door.

Lots of furniture was being unloaded from a huge van outside

"Look Jack!" said his Mum, "I think our new neighbours have arrived."

Jack was concentrating on the computer screen and hardly heard what his Mum had said.

The next day, as Mum walked to the postbox, she passed the house next door and saw a woman cleaning the windows.

Jack's Mum waved and said,

"Hello! We're your next-door neighbours. Welcome to the street."

"I would invite you in," said the woman, "but the house is in a complete mess."

"Don't worry," said Jack's Mum, "why don't you come round this afternoon and take a break?"

"I'd love to," said the woman, "and may I bring Simon, my son?"

"Of course," said Jack's Mum, "he can meet Jack."

Simon and his Mum arrived later that afternoon and Jack's first question to Simon was,

"Do you like computer games?"

Within minutes, they were both concentrating on the screen – and Jack was winning.

After three or four games – all of which Jack won – Simon said, "Come on Jack, let's go out on our bikes – you can show me around, you must know all the places we can go."

Jack frowned. His bike was rusty with flat tyres and he didn't really know any places to go.

"No I can't," he said, embarrassed, "sorry."

Simon looked a bit disappointed and left soon afterwards with his Mum.

The doorbell rang early the next morning.
Jack's Mum went to the door.

Jack was watching television in his room and his Mum had to shout to get his attention.

"Jack, it's Simon from next door."

"Tell him to come up," replied Jack, stretching himself lazily, not particularly wanting to be disturbed.

BOOM

As soon as Simon appeared at the door, Jack asked him,

"Which is your favourite cartoon? There's this great programme on where they show bits of all the best ones, it's on now."

"I can't stay," said Simon, "Mum's outside and we're taking Turnip for his first walk around his new neighbourhood and wondered if you would like to come with us?"

"Turnip?" said Jack, "I thought you ate that, not took it for a walk."

"This Turnip is a man-eating Yorkshire Terrier," said Simon. "And if you're not careful, he'll eat you!"

"Walking's boring," said Jack, still watching the screen.

"Please yourself," said Simon,

"we are going to the park where there are all sorts of things we can do."

"That's less boring, I suppose," said Jack, following Simon downstairs. Jack was not entirely sure that it might be too much of an effort but did not want to appear lazy.

"I'm going for a walk with Simon and Turnip," said Jack to his Mum, who opened her mouth to say something and then thought better of it!

The park was huge. Jack had only been once before. They found lots of sticks for Turnip to chase. In the corner was a big old tree.

"Come on!" said Simon, "Let's see who can climb the highest."

Simon climbed higher than Jack but they both laughed when Turnip stood at the bottom of the tree, barking and barking at them until they came down.

They tried the climbing frames, swung on the ropes and crawled through the wooden tunnel, with Turnip close behind!

On the way home, Jack said to Simon,
"That was good fun today with Turnip,
can I come with you again?"

"What are you doing on Sunday?" said Simon,
"Because my friend Grace is coming over and
we are going cycling. You could come too."
Jack heard himself saying he'd love to.

Sunday was a clear day – which was a good thing because Jack had spent most of Saturday cleaning his bike – and the three of them set off together.

Simon was in the lead. Grace pedalled hard to keep up with him and Jack puffed along last. "Come along Jack," said Simon, "you can't be slower than a girl!"

He was, but he realised that if he put in some more effort, he would be as fast as his new friends. He suddenly felt a confidence that he had not experienced before and he was really enjoying himself!

When Jack got home that evening his Mum said,

"You've got rosy cheeks!"
in the way that Mums do,
but Jack had to admit
he felt good; tired but good.

So tired in fact that he missed
one of his favourite shows on television that night.

When his Dad heard about Jack's day, he
told him about how he had cycled a lot
when he was younger.

"Well," said Jack,
"then you can come
with me next time!"

Over the following weeks, Jack and Simon became close friends, playing indoors and out. Now and then, they would watch television or play on the computer. But Jack no longer won the computer games all the time and Simon didn't always climb the highest tree.

And, Jack was still winning the cycling challenges set by his Dad, but his Dad was definitely catching up!

TEN HELPFUL HINTS
FOR PARENTS TO KEEP THEIR CHILDREN ACTIVE

by Dr. Richard Woolfson

1. Build physical activity into your child's normal daily routine. Rather than making exercise something special for your child, encourage him to walk to school, to play outdoors and so on.

2. Set a good example yourself. If you follow a healthy lifestyle, your child will follow suit. Good physical habits established in childhood will last into adulthood.

3. Make physical exercise fun. There is no reason why walking, for example, can't be part of a family outing to somewhere special.

4. Try to limit the amount of time your child spends sitting in front of the computer or television. Agree a daily limit for these activities and do your best to ensure your child sticks to it.

5. Suggest after-school activity classes. Physical exercise is included in a range of leisure interests, not just sport, for instance, dance and drama classes where he'll enjoy mixing with others too.

6. Make sure that your child takes part in physical exercise classes in school. He needs to know that you expect him to take part and that you won't help him to avoid it.

7. Find out about local facilities and then discuss these with your child. Suggest that he at least tries one of those available in his area. Let him choose which one to attend.

8. Give him active household chores such as taking the rubbish outside to the bin, picking up debris from the lawn or washing the family car. Every bit of exercise helps.

9. Emphasise the benefits of exercise. Explain to him that it keeps his heart healthy and gives him good muscles and strong bones.

10. Buy toys that involve physical activity. A bat and ball, a tennis racket, a climbing frame, a small trampoline for the garden, or a swing are all popular toys that encourage exercise.

The helping hand books